THE STORY BEHIND THE BEANO BOOK COVER

# DENNIS THE MENACE IN ROBOT RUMBLE!

I'VE BEEN TUNING UP MY BRILLIANT MENACECAR.

WONDER IF OUR NEW TURBO-BOOST ENGINE WORKS?

ROAR! VOOM!

W-WOW! IT CERTAINLY DOES!

Back in Beanotown —

# GENERAL JUMBO

Jumbo Johnson was the proud owner of an army of radio-controlled models. One day, he took them to the school canteen.

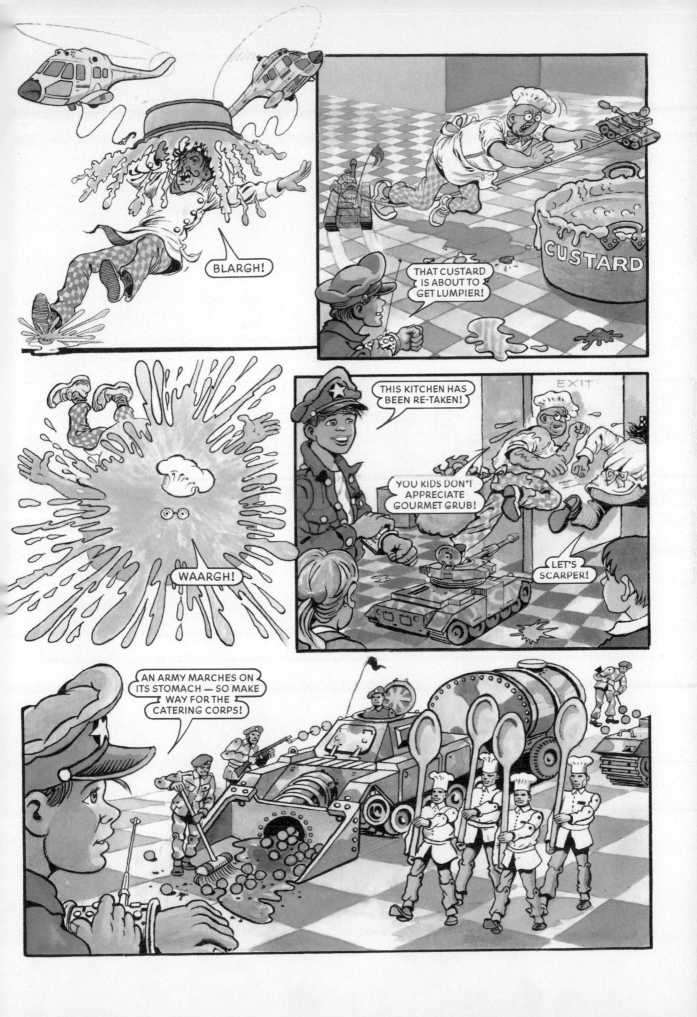

The tank regiment roll out pastry.

The cooks make soup.

And the victors enjoy a good meal!

Next day —

HEY, READERS! ANSWER THE FOLLOWING QUESTIONNAIRE TO FIND OUT IF YOU SHOULD BE . . .

# . . . LICENSED TO MENACE

IN A POSH RESTAURANT YOU ARE OFFERED SPROUTS WITH YOUR MEAL. DO YOU —

a. TAKE THE SPROUTS AND USE A PUDDING SPOON TO FIRE THEM AT THE WAITER?

b. TAKE THE SPROUTS AND FEED YOUR PET PIG UNDER THE TABLE?

C. ASK FOR THEM TO BE LIQUIDISED IN CASE YOU DAMAGE YOUR TOOTHY-PEGS?

YOU ARE ASKED BY MUM TO MAKE YOUR BED. DO YOU —

a. MAKE YOUR BED . . . INTO A PIRATE SHIP AND LAUNCH IT DOWN THE STAIRS?

b. MOAN ABOUT HAVING TO DO IT FOR TWELVE HOURS? (TILL IT'S BED-TIME AGAIN)

C. DO SO WITH A HAPPY SMILE AND EMBROIDER PINK BUNNIES ON THE DUVET?

**YOUR DAD TELLS YOU TO DO YOUR HOMEWORK FOR SCHOOL. DO YOU —**

**a.** SAY YOU'LL DO A SPOT OF HISTORY AND RE-ENACT THE BATTLE OF TRAFALGAR?

**b.** SAY YOU'RE STUDYING AUSTRALIA IN GEOGRAPHY AND WATCH "NEIGHBOURS"?

**C.** WRITE AN ESSAY CALLED "WHY I LOVE TEDDY" THEN SKIP ROUND TO HELP YOUR FRIENDS DO *THEIR* HOMEWORK?

SKIP!

**YOU GET COVERED IN MUD IN AN ACCIDENTAL MUD FIGHT. DO YOU —**

**a.** ROLL ABOUT ON THE HAIRDRESSER'S FLOOR, THEN PRETEND TO BE A GORILLA?

HAIR SALON

**b.** RUB THE MUD OFF WITH DAD'S TOWELLING DRESSING-GOWN?

BATH-ROOM

**C.** COVER YOURSELF IN PANSY SEEDS SO YOU CAN GROW PRETTY FLOWERS ALL OVER YOURSELF?

**IT'S BEEN SNOWING HEAVILY OVERNIGHT. DO YOU —**

**a.** BUILD A HUGE SNOWMAN ON THE END OF A SEESAW, THEN LAUNCH IT AT THE PARKIE?

FLUMP!

THUD!

**b.** PUT ON CRICKET GEAR SO MUM CAN'T SEE YOU WHEN SHE CALLS YOU IN OUT OF THE COLD!

**C.** WRAP YOURSELF IN ALL THE CLOTHES YOU OWN AND KNIT TEDDY A COSY JUMP-SUIT?

SHAKE!

CHATTER!

CLICK

YOU'VE FORGOTTEN MUM'S BIRTHDAY AGAIN. DO YOU —

a. WAIT TILL DAD FALLS ASLEEP THEN WRAP HIM IN PAPER?

STICK!

To mum

b. GIVE HER A PICTURE OF A GOLD NECKLACE — IT'S THE THOUGHT THAT COUNTS?

c. SMACK YOURSELF LIMPLY — ON THE BOTTOM FOR BEING SO THOUGHTLESS?

LIMP SMACK!

HOW DID YOU DO? ALL a.'s — YOU'RE A GRADE ONE MENACE YOU MAY FILL IN YOUR NAME ON YOUR LICENCE TO MENACE FORM.

MAINLY b.'s — YOU'RE WELL ON THE WAY TO BECOMING A MENACE — GET YOURSELF A BIT MORE ATTITUDE!

ALL c.'s — OH, DEAR!

BET THAT SCARED YOU!

RAZZ!

_ _ _ _ _ _ _ _ _ _

IS VERY NAUGHTY INDEED AND IS HEREBY

**LICENCED to MENACE**

signed

dennis

PEAS

and

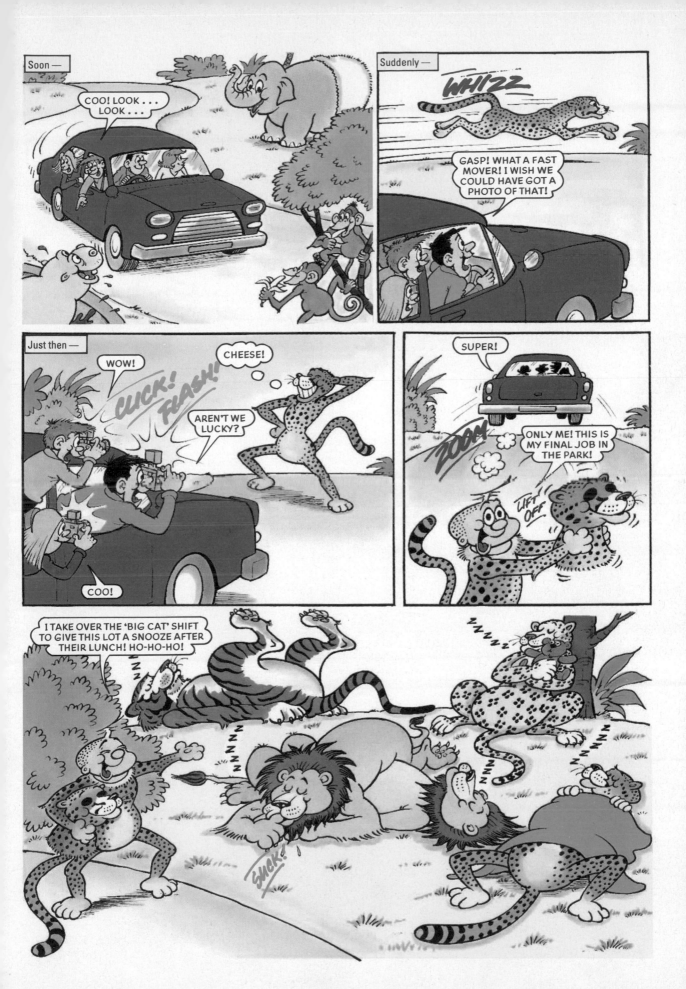

# Joe King's
# Wild Joke Page

A crocodile bit me on the leg once.

Really? which one?

I dunno – all crocodiles look the same to me!

How do you stop a rhino charging? Take away his credit card!

What did the snail say when he climbed onto the tortoise?

Slow Down! Slow Down!

PLUG Is So Ugly...
. . . WHEN IT WAS HIS TURN TO HAVE HIS SCHOOL PHOTO TAKEN, THE CAMERA RAN AWAY!
I'M OFF!
. . . HE GETS VALENTINE CARDS — FROM WARTHOGS!
BE MY VALENTINE
. . . THE JANITOR USES HIM AS A WEEDKILLER!
WILT
WILT
WILT
WILT
. . . TOOTS KNITTED HIM A 'SPECIAL' BALACLAVA!
YOU FORGOT TO LEAVE A HOLE.
HEE-HEE!
. . . HE HAS A PART-TIME JOB TURNING MILK INTO YOGHURT!

WAHEY! SNOW! PERFECT DODGE CONDITIONS.

Reader's voice.

ER, NOT TOO LOUD, ROGER.

GROOGH! OF COURSE — IT'S A DODGY TIME FOR AVALANCHES!

FLUMP!

I'LL BLAST MY WAY OUT WITH A HOT AIR DODGE.

BLAST OF HOT AIR!

THE WAY IS CLEAR FOR SOME SLEDGING DODGES NOW.

HO-HO! MUSKY IS A HUSKY. HE LOVES THE SNOW. MUSH! MUSH!

I CAN'T GO MUSH FASTER, ROGER.

SWOOSH!

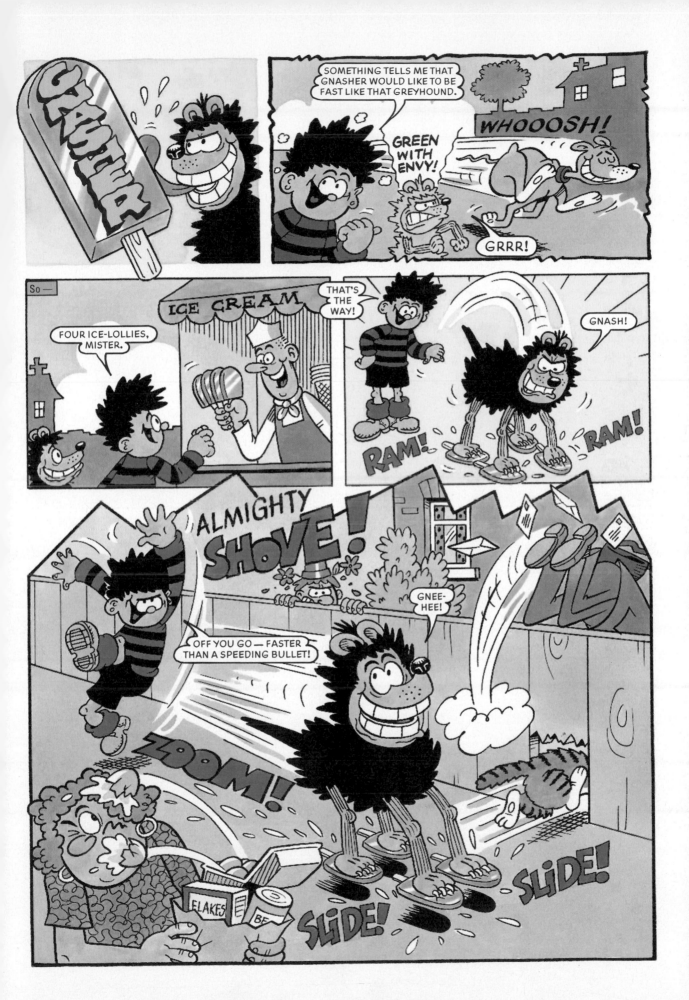

THAT'S ME!

# GORDON BENNETT!

Mr. Nimby.

I'M OFF TO BEANOTOWN THEATRE.

YES! LETS! ME GET ON WITH MY GARDENING IN PERFECT PEACE.

NO POINT IN SPENDING MY POCKET-MONEY. I'LL SNEAK IN.

BACK DOOR

TODAY THE GREAT ZAPPO HYPNOTIST

Soon —

HEH-HEH! I'VE GOT THE BEST VIEW IN THE HOUSE.

YOU ARE FEELING SLEEPY . . . SLEEPY . . . YOU THINK YOU ARE A DOG . . .

DON'T TALK DAFT — YOU'RE HOPELESS, YOU ARE.

I SAY!

WHUMP!

Oh-oh! Looks like Zappo's act has worked on our Gordon!

WOOF!

WHUFF!

WOW! SHAKING NOW! HE MUST HAVE A CHILL!

WAH!

BOOME!

HA-HA! RASHER WAS ONLY SHAKING WITH EXCITEMENT!

SPLUTCH!

NEIGHBOUR'S VEGETABLE COMPOST HEAP

HMM! GREEN PIG . . . HUMPH . . . VERY ODD . . .

At the Vet's.

ALL ABOUT PIGS

I'LL SOUND HIM OUT!

Back home —

OH, BEA!

AHA! MUM'S FOUND OUT THAT BEA'S BEEN PAINTING. HO-HO!

YOUR LITTLE SISTER, BEA! CHUCKLE!

HAW-HAW! SO BEA'S PAINTED RASHER GREEN!

HI, CUTHBERT CRINGEWORTHY, BOY GENIUS, HERE. LOOK THROUGH MY MAGNIFYING-GLASS AND YOU CAN SEE ANOTHER WORLD. THE WORLD OF....
THE BEANO BUGS
NICE

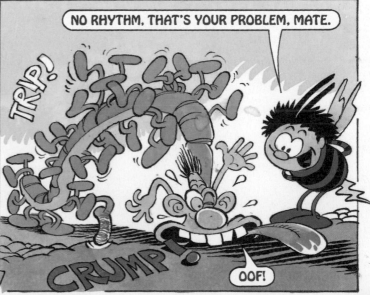

THE DANCE CONTINUES IN A COUPLE OF PAGES!

# BITS ABOUT BUGS

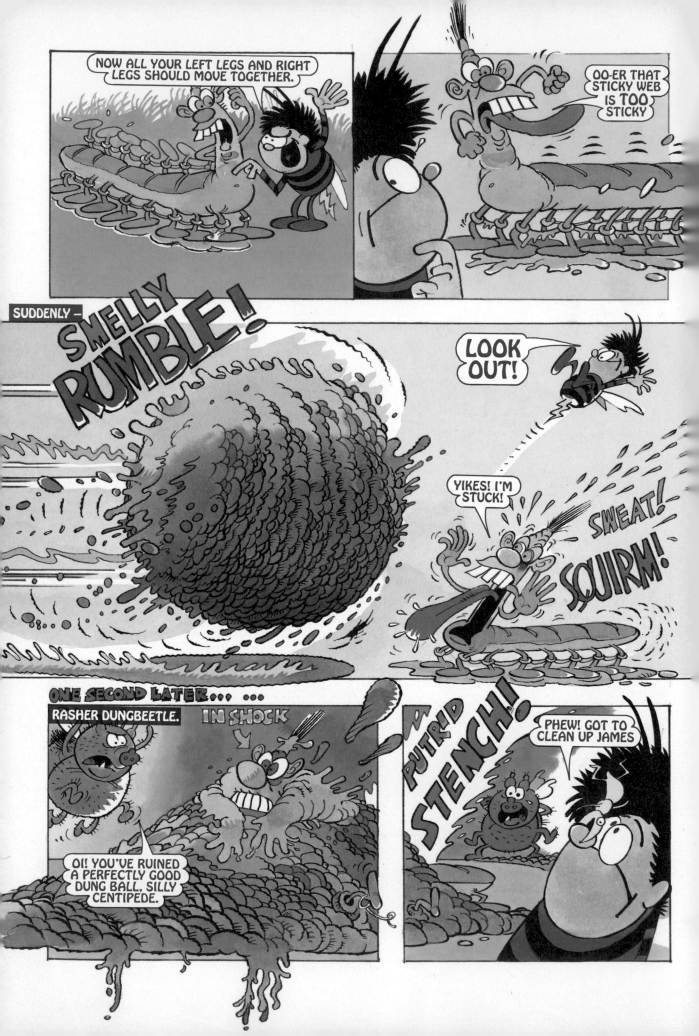

# The BEANO STARS ON A ROLL

I'M BORED!

ME TOO!

ME THREE!

Suddenly —

HISSS!

THUD!

A CHALLENGE WE SHALL NOT REFUSE!

WE THROW DOWN THE IN-LINE SKATING GAUNTLET TO THE BEANO STARS SIGNED— THE EAGLES

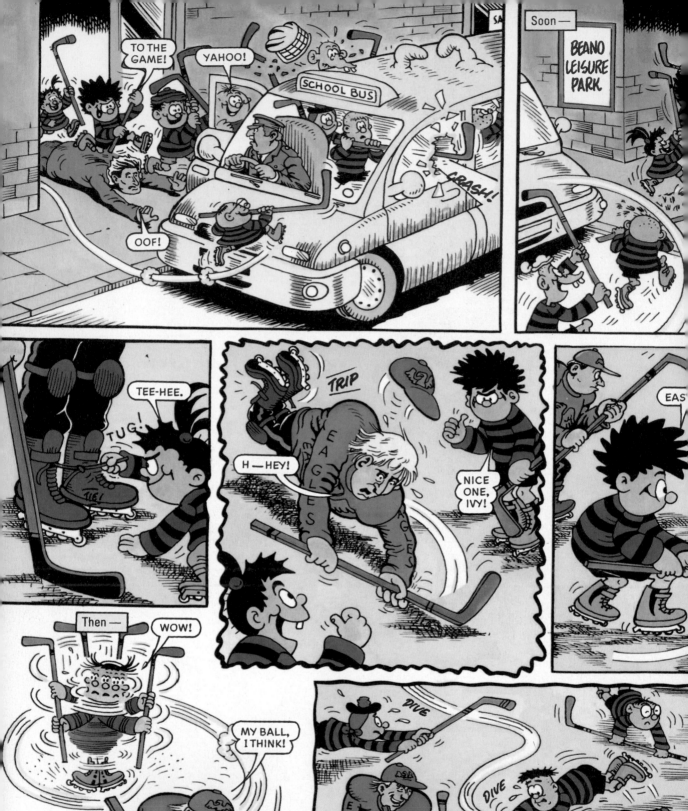

# THE NUMSKULLS

BRAINY, BLINKY, RADAR, CRUNCHER and SNITCH. They're

Edd looks really puzzled!

UH?

SNIFF!

LEAVE IT TO ME! I'LL LISTEN FOR THE MISSING PIECE.

BUGS

YOU'RE A TWIT! YOU'RE A TWIT!

LEAP!

Now Mum looks really puzzled!

ANSWERS

BLINKY — Snitch's tongue, Brainy's glasses, Radar's hands, Cruncher's nose. CRUNCHER — Only eat the table!!!! BRAINY — (a) Dennis, (b) Minnie, (c) Smiffy, (d) Walter. SNITCH — (a) Granny, (b) Teacher, (c) Rasher, (d) Gnasher, (e) Plug. RADAR — (a) Tower Bridge, (b) The Eiffel Tower, (c) The Houses of Parliament.

# LES PRETEND

## THE LITTLE KID WITH THE BIG IMAGINATION

SWING!

With skates on his feet and lasso
in his hand
Young Dennis hoped he'd be in luck.
Just then came the sound of the
flapping of wings
'Twas Egbert a large, dopey duck.

WHEEE!

As planned, Egbert soon found his way to the park,
With our menace mates firmly in tow.
The Softies were having a nice picnic lunch —
Our heroes destroyed their gateaux.

NO SWIMMING ALLOWED

The Parkie ran up and yelled at our Den
"No swimming allowed! Stop
your clowning!"
Spurting out tadpoles our hero replied,
"No swimming — well, how about drowning?"

No pies and no cakes for wet Dennis to eat —
The dip in the pond made them soggy.
So all that was left for the Menace to do
Was share lunch with his little doggy!

TAKE THAT HAT OFF IN CLASS.

BUT, SIR . . .

LEAP!

SQUEAK!

. . . MINNIE, MY MOUSE, SLEEPS UNDER THERE.

OH, NO!

STAND IN THE CORNER, GIRL!

PERFECT FOR MORE OUTSTANDING MINXING.

TIME FOR SOME SHERBET FIZZO IN THE STAFF'S TEA.

STAFF ROOM

ZZZ

SPLUTTER!

I DON'T THINK THIS JOB'S QUITE HIS CUP OF TEA!

GROAN!

STAFF ROOM

THIS WAY, SIR. I'LL SHOW YOU TO THE, ER, STAFF ROOM.

BILLY WHIZZ Is So Fast...
. . . HE ACTS AS PACEMAKER FOR WORLD LAND SPEED RECORD ATTEMPTS!
WORLD RECORD ATTEMPT
HURRY UP! FASTER! FASTER!
. . . HE CAN JUMP OUT OF BED, PUT OUT THE LIGHT AND BE UNDER THE DUVET BEFORE IT'S DARK!
. . . HE ONCE RAN A LAP OF BEANOTOWN TRACK AND OVERTOOK HIMSELF!
WELL RUN ME!
. . . HE WON THE LE MANS TWENTY FOUR HOUR RACE— IN HIS PEDAL CAR!
. . . HE MAKES DELIVERIES FOR A CHINESE RESTAURANT — FROM BEIJING!
ORDER FOR BLOGGS!

# BEHIND THE MASK!

# FUN and GAMES with DENNIS the MENACE

"**T**his is it! This is it!" yelled Dennis last summer as he ripped open a letter which had just been delivered by a man dressed in a suit of armour and carrying a bazooka and a machine-gun (the postie had been 'introduced' to Gnasher before, you see!)

"This ISN'T it! This ISN'T it!" moaned Dennis, his face dropping. Gnasher picked up Dennis's face, licked it then gave it back to his beloved master.

"Huh!" said The Menace once his fizzog was firmly back in place. "I offered myself to the British Olympic Committee for the team for Sydney, but something tells me I'm not wanted. That something was the letter he'd just received stating in large bold letters WE DON'T WANT YOU! Signed The Olympic Committee.

Dennis gritted his teeth (you can't be too careful with so much frost around).

"OK!" he muttered. "If they won't let me go to The Olympic Games, I'll hold my very own Menace Games right here in Beanotown."

Not just anyone was selected to compete in The Menace Olympics. Oh, no . . . only very special people — those Dennis could beat!

Dear Dennis
WE DON'T WANT YOU!
Your chums,
The Olympic Committee.

Not surprisingly these included Dennis's sworn enemies (Language, DENNIS!). Walter and the Softies.

Unfortunately this was to prove Dennis's downfall — literally, cos he fell over in shock when he saw the namby-pamby way the Softies took part in the competition.

Now, the hop, step and jump is a fine event but the Softies insisted on making it a hop, skip and prance — hopeless!

When it was Dennis' turn to show how to do things properly, he found that Bertie Blenkinsop had produced a lovely lace tablecloth and was having a picnic for his favourite teddies in the jump pit. Dennis found this out when he landed on, and seriously injured, poor Mr Fluffy-wuffy.

The 100 metres never got going because, to protect their delicate ear-drums from nasty loud noises, the Softies stuffed wads of pink cotton-wool in their lugholes. Of course, they didn't hear a thing when the starting pistol sounded. Perhaps it was just as well they didn't hear the very rude names Dennis called them.

Next came the discus event. You guessed it, the puny Softies couldn't lift the nasty, heavy discus off the ground and had to change the competition to 'skimming the paper plates'.

At least Dennis had some fun with this event as he loaded his paper plates with cream buns and over-ripe tomatoes. Even the Softies' best ballet moves failed to prevent them getting hit by flying foodstuff.

It was a pity that the next event was the steeplechase, cos Walter and his chummies used the water-jump to give their stained clothes a wash through and completely ruined the race in a cloud of soap suds.

The whole day became a farce (Dennis half expected a vicar to run and drop his trousers). The javelin became 'toss the cocktail stick', the pentathlon events comprised of needlework, dusting, fairy cake making, hard sums and cuddling and when the synchronised swimming because synchronised simpering Dennis had had quite enough.

The Menace was beside himself. Being beside himself he turned to his likeness and said — "That's it, Dennis — it's time for the medal ceremony."

"Oh, goody!" trilled Walter. "I do believe we've won every event."

Soon the Softies' flags were being run up the flagpoles to the gentle strains of the Softy anthem "Land of Soap and Dollies".

Mind you, the music was soon drowned out by the sound of squeals and shrieks . . . guess who had tied the Softies' ankles to the flags?!!

Har-har! You got it in one!

# PAWS FOR THOUGHT

Can you match the words with the pictures, Readers? The fir[st] one is done for you to give you a start. Answers at the foot of the page

MUDDY TODAY! ● ICE ON THE GARDEN PATH! ● TIME FOR A CLAW TRIM! ● HOPE DAD DOESN'T NOTICE THAT CHEWED TABLE LEG! ● I AM *NOT* GOING TO THE VETS'! ● RIVERDANCE?–'S EASY!

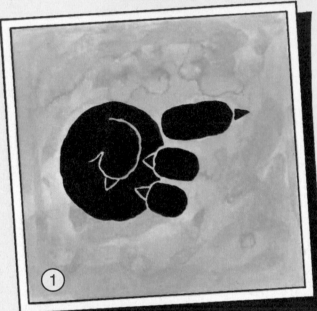

1

2

HE WENT THAT AWAY!

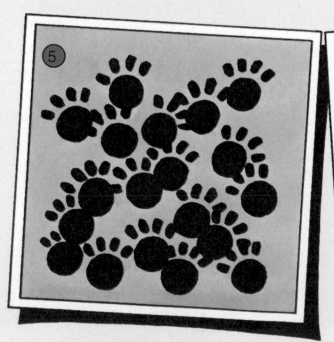

5

6

## ANSWERS

THIS ISN'T PART OF THE PUZZLE. IT'S MY AUTOGRAPH FOR ALL YOU GNASHER FANS OUT THERE!

# LES PRETEND

# LOOK OUT FOR DENNIS and GNASHER!

THE WORLD'S WILDEST BOY AND HIS FAITHFUL HOUND ARE HAVING A DAY OUT AT BEANOTOWN BEACH. ENJOY THE FUN IN THE SUN AND SEE IF YOU CAN SPOT DENNIS AND GNASHER IN THE PICTURE.